D1621687

AWESOME PUZZLES FOR CLEVER KIDS

Welcome!

This book belongs to:

_____

Thank you for choosing our Awesome Puzzles Book. It's great to see that you enjoy doing these activities as much as we do!

This is a big workbook! It was made for you to make sure you get to do all the activities you could ever want. It'll offer hours of entertainment and a refreshing way to both unplug and improve your brain functions through coloring, hand-eye coordination, problem solving, and so much more!

BIRDS WORD SEARCH

Find all the hidden words that are listed below. Words can be up, down, or forward.

S	V	L	Q	G	Z	B	C	V	M
T	H	N	F	O	B	N	D	S	M
O	F	O	P	O	C	P	H	P	P
R	H	P	Y	S	R	E	L	A	A
K	S	N	V	E	O	A	K	R	R
Q	W	Q	C	D	W	C	P	R	R
A	A	P	I	G	E	O	N	O	O
L	N	D	O	V	E	C	U	W	T
T	U	R	K	E	Y	K	L	I	Y
D	I	Q	M	L	I	A	G	X	E

CROW
PEACOCK
DOVE
SPARROW
GOOSE

PIGEON
TURKEY
PARROT
SWAN
STORK

MAZE PUZZLE

Help the owl find a way to the acorn!

MUSIC

The party is about to start, help the band to
find the musical instruments' shadows.

FIND 10 DIFFERENCES

MATH SEARCH

Certain numbers in this puzzle, when added together,
will make a total that matches the given sum in the center.
The numbers must be connected horizontally, vertically or diagonally.
The connected numbers must be in one straight line.

7	3	4	4	1	4	9	6
7	2	2	4	2	6	6	7
8	8	4	5	8	2	2	1
9	7	2	20		5	7	8
1	2	4			5	9	2
1	6	5	7	3	3	7	8
5	1	5	8	8	8	8	4
8	6	2	5	6	8	1	5

You can find 11 ways
to make a sum of
20 in this puzzle.

(One of the 11 answers has
been done for you!)

You can find 17 ways
to make a sum of
10 in this puzzle.

(One of the 17 answers has
been done for you!)

9	5	2	4	9	4	2	8
4	1	2	2	3	6	7	5
3	5	3	5	9	5	9	5
1	8	3	10		1	1	4
7	4	8			6	5	4
5	1	5	4	9	6	8	5
6	7	7	9	5	3	1	1
2	8	1	6	4	1	2	6

MAZE PUZZLE

Help the lion find a way the cub!

SCRAMBLED WORDS

Unscramble the words with the help of pictures.
(the pictures may not be next to the right words!)

WIKI _____

ONLME _____

ENOARG _____

HPCEA _____

BSTRWARYRE _____

NANAABS _____

SGPERA _____

NMGAO _____

MARTWELENO _____

ELPPA _____

FOLLOW THE PATTERNS

Color the shape that comes next.

TRANSPORTATION CROSSWORD

Complete the crossword puzzle by filling in the appropriate letters with the help of pictures given below.

DOWN

ACROSS

COLORING ADDITION

Find the sum for each addition problem. Use the sum to find the correct color listed below.

Blue = 8   Red = 10   Black = 9

Brown = 7   Pink = 5

SCHOOL

Help the students to find the shadows.

FIND 10 DIFFERENCES

MATH SEARCH

Certain numbers in this puzzle, when added together,
will make a total that matches the given sum in the center.
The numbers must be connected horizontally, vertically or diagonally.
The connected numbers must be in one straight line.

6	3	1	2	9	8	9	8
9	3	2	2	8	9	6	7
7	7	9	5	5	5	7	7
4	9	7	**27**		9	3	1
4	8	8			4	5	6
8	1	9	1	4	6	1	8
4	8	8	4	7	9	5	8
3	6	3	9	6	3	2	8

You can find 10 ways
to make a sum of
27 in this puzzle.

(One of the 10 answers has
been done for you!)

You can find 13 ways
to make a sum of
22 in this puzzle.

(One of the 13 answers has
been done for you!)

5	3	4	5	8	4	8	5
6	2	7	2	6	7	5	9
7	8	3	1	9	1	6	3
9	6	6	**22**		7	8	8
6	1	5			1	3	9
6	5	4	9	1	4	8	2
4	3	5	6	1	5	9	4
1	1	2	9	7	6	4	7

FLOWERS WORD SEARCH

Find all the hidden words that are listed below. Words can be up, down, or forward.

U	J	L	Q	W	D	W	V	X	S
N	A	I	A	Q	A	P	L	D	G
A	S	L	T	X	F	A	O	A	G
K	M	Y	U	R	F	N	T	I	X
I	I	K	L	O	O	S	U	S	V
V	N	S	I	S	D	Y	S	Y	C
I	E	G	P	E	I	Q	O	W	G
Y	S	U	N	F	L	O	W	E	R
V	O	R	C	H	I	D	X	H	Y
Q	L	F	G	R	U	P	C	U	S

ROSE
PANSY
JASMINE
LILY
LOTUS

TULIP
ORCHID
DAISY
DAFFODIL
SUNFLOWER

16

MAZE PUZZLE

Help the monkey find a way to the bananas!

SCRAMBLED WORDS

Unscramble the words with the help of pictures.
(the pictures may not be next to the right words!)

RTEE _____

ITUGAR _____

SNU _____

EBTCUK _____

CIRHA _____

PLIECN _____

ARCMIECE _____

CNDYA _____

LALB _____

EBLMRULA _____

FOLLOW THE PATTERNS

Color the butterfly that comes next.

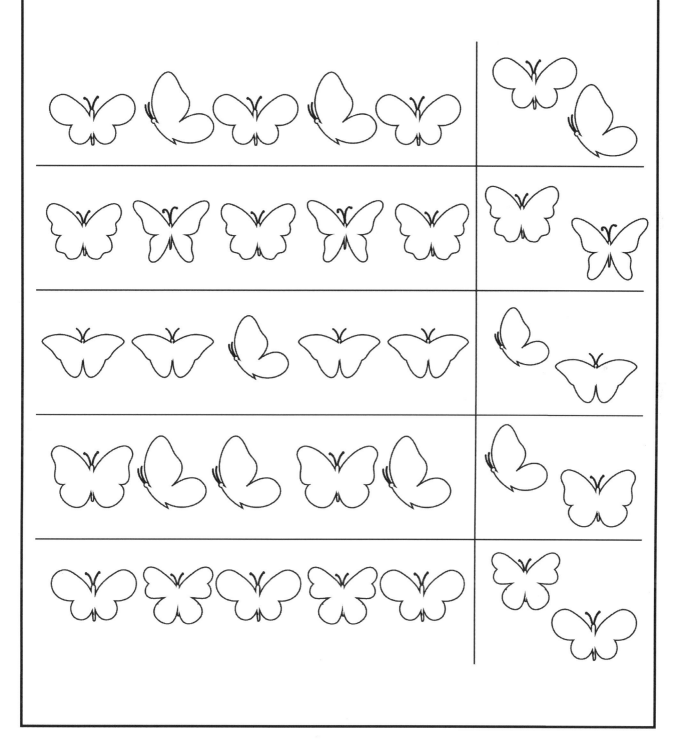

CROSSWORD PUZZLE

Complete the crossword puzzle by filling in the appropriate letters with the help of words listed below.

BELIEVE
DEPENDABLE
EMPOWER
FOCUS
HAPPY

IMAGINATION
KNOWLEDGE
MOTIVATED
OUTSTANDING
POSITIVITY

COLORING ADDITION

Find the sum for each addition problem. Use the sum to find the correct color listed below.

Blue = 11   Green = 9   Yellow = 13   Orange = 16

Brown = 10   Black = 17   Pink = 7

21

ZOO

Welcome to the zoo! Try to find the shadows.

FIND 10 DIFFERENCES

23

MATH SEARCH

Certain numbers in this puzzle, when added together,
will make a total that matches the given sum in the center.

The numbers must be connected horizontally, vertically or diagonally.

The connected numbers must be in one straight line.

9	1	6	1	9	7	7	2
3	3	1	5	7	4	9	7
2	4	1	3	6	9	3	1
9	4	8	15		6	5	9
5	5	6			8	5	5
8	6	4	6	6	6	6	5
9	3	6	8	2	3	3	8
4	3	5	9	8	5	9	8

You can find 13 ways
to make a sum of
15 in this puzzle.

(One of the 13 answers has
been done for you!)

You can find 10 ways
to make a sum of
29 in this puzzle.

(One of the 10 answers has
been done for you!)

7	6	5	2	1	3	7	9
4	4	2	8	5	6	4	9
3	7	6	6	8	2	4	6
5	9	6	29		3	9	9
1	6	7			9	2	6
2	6	1	7	9	8	5	6
9	2	6	7	3	7	5	1
3	7	8	8	4	2	7	7

SEA CREATURE WORD SEARCH

Find all the hidden words that are listed below. Words can be up, down, or forward.

D	O	L	P	H	I	N	Q	G	U
W	Q	S	F	V	V	V	F	V	Y
I	V	E	I	K	S	Q	U	I	D
S	D	A	S	X	J	V	H	B	O
H	C	L	H	S	H	E	L	L	S
A	R	U	Z	S	H	R	I	M	P
R	A	Q	J	O	Y	S	T	E	R
K	B	V	J	H	E	J	S	D	V
O	C	T	O	P	U	S	G	J	V
J	I	R	M	Y	X	Y	D	Y	B

CRAB
FISH
OCTOPUS
OYSTER
SEAL

DOLPHIN
SHARK
SHRIMP
SHELLS
SQUID

MAZE PUZZLE

Help the bee find a way to the flower!

SCRAMBLED WORDS

Unscramble the words with the help of pictures.
(the pictures may not be next to the right words!)

HFIS   _____

APC   _____

TRYETLUFB   _____

EBE   _____

ZAPZI   _____

OTMAOT   _____

URDM   _____

REKOTC   _____

DGO   _____

KBOO   _____

FOLLOW THE PATTERNS

Color the flower that comes next.

CROSSWORD PUZZLE

Complete the crossword puzzle by filling in the appropriate letters with the help of words listed below.

I			
U			
T			
L		O	A

CHILD   ROOM   POLICE
GIRL   COOKIE   STUDY
HOME   ROAD   SCHOOL
BOY   BIRD   YEAR
STORY   APPLE   RING

COLORING ADDITION

Find the sum for each addition problem. Use the sum to find the correct color listed below.

Blue = 13   Red = 16   Black = 11

Pink = 18   Green = 15   Brown = 14

DINOSAUR

We are back to the cretaceous period.
Try to find the dinosaurs' shadows.

MATH SEARCH

Certain numbers in this puzzle, when added together,
will make a total that matches the given sum in the center.
The numbers must be connected horizontally, vertically or diagonally.
The connected numbers must be in one straight line.

7	7	6	6	6	2	9	5
1	8	4	5	1	1	2	6
7	4	5	7	4	5	5	7
7	9	2	**30**		4	2	2
7	7	4			9	1	1
9	7	2	7	4	3	4	2
9	7	7	3	9	5	8	3
1	1	5	5	6	3	7	2

You can find 6 ways
to make a sum of
30 in this puzzle.

(One of the 6 answers has
been done for you!)

You can find 14 ways
to make a sum of
12 in this puzzle.

(One of the 14 answers has
been done for you!)

1	7	6	4	3	3	3	8
2	4	8	3	5	3	3	7
1	7	8	5	8	8	1	2
3	8	6	**12**		8	1	8
2	6	9			7	5	6
2	2	8	6	7	9	1	6
7	6	3	2	9	4	9	5
9	9	6	9	7	6	1	6

SPRING WORD SEARCH

Find all the hidden words that are listed below. Words can be up, down, or forward.

S	A	B	Z	F	C	F	M	F	B
P	I	T	U	L	I	P	D	Q	E
R	Q	T	N	O	H	V	P	Y	E
I	V	B	X	W	W	K	I	Z	D
N	K	I	T	E	O	V	C	D	J
G	S	R	K	R	R	W	N	Q	Q
R	T	D	Q	W	M	R	I	K	J
A	Y	Y	F	D	X	T	C	W	M
S	P	J	R	A	I	N	J	R	C
S	V	U	U	T	R	E	E	U	C

SPRING
TREE
BEE
BIRD
FLOWER

PICNIC
RAIN
GRASS
WORM
TULIP

34

MAZE PUZZLE

Help the caterpillar find a way to the leaf!

SCRAMBLED WORDS

Unscramble the words, which are sea animals.
(the pictures may not be next to the right words!)

SFISRHTA

_____

ERAOSSHE

_____

BCAR

_____

SFHI

_____

UOCPOTS

_____

FHSLIYEJL

_____

LHELS

_____

OIHLPND

_____

LTETUR

_____

EHWAL

_____

FOLLOW THE PATTERNS

Color the shape that comes next.

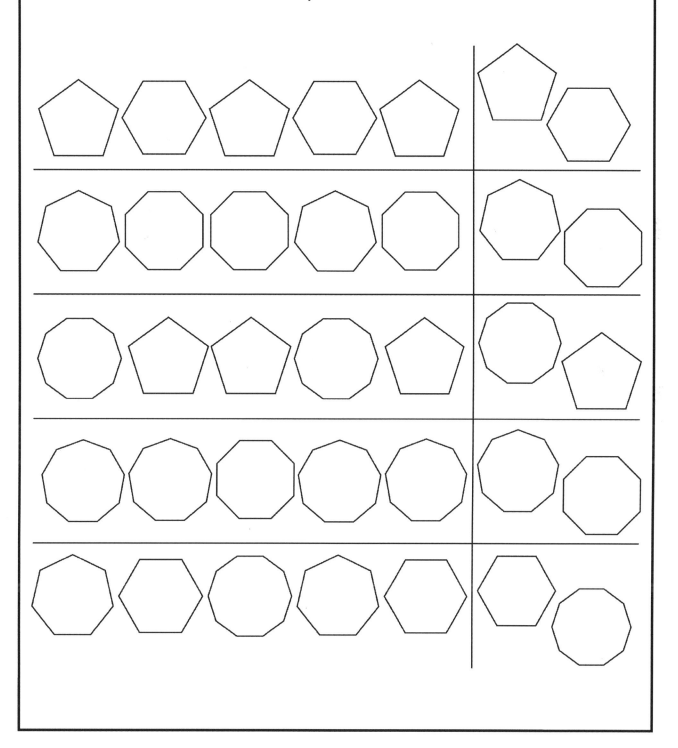

37

FOOD CROSSWORD

Complete the crossword puzzle by filling in the appropriate letters with the help of words listed below.

ALMONDS   CASHEWS
APPLES   CELERY
BEANS   CHEESE
BLUEBERRY   CHICKEN
BROWNRICE   CORN

COLORING ADDITION

Find the sum for each addition problem. Use the sum to find the correct color listed below.

Orange = 17   Blue = 20   Red = 15   Black = 9

Gray = 14   Green = 10   Brown = 12

39

SPACE

Let's take a trip to space. Try to find
the right shadows.

MATH SEARCH

Certain numbers in this puzzle, when added together,
will make a total that matches the given sum in the center.

The numbers must be connected horizontally, vertically or diagonally.

The connected numbers must be in one straight line.

8	5	8	5	6	8	7	4
6	5	3	4	1	5	5	9
2	2	3	6	2	7	7	8
1	4	8		**26**		8	1	7
3	8	9			3	2	1
4	8	4	5	4	4	1	2
5	9	6	9	7	3	6	7
9	4	8	9	4	7	7	5

You can find 7 ways
to make a sum of
26 in this puzzle.

(One of the 7 answers has
been done for you!)

You can find 6 ways
to make a sum of
33 in this puzzle.

(One of the 6 answers has
been done for you!)

9	9	9	9	3	9	4	5
2	8	6	7	6	8	9	7
4	8	4	4	6	5	5	2
5	2	5		**33**		8	1	1
5	2	7			1	3	9
2	4	1	5	5	7	2	7
8	3	8	2	8	1	7	1
9	8	2	1	3	2	2	5

WEATHER WORD SEARCH

Find all the hidden words that are listed below. Words can be up, down, or forward.

G	T	F	O	G	M	I	S	T	X
W	H	P	L	D	X	D	I	J	N
C	U	E	P	R	V	Y	S	I	U
L	N	L	W	I	N	D	U	O	O
O	D	D	V	Z	A	O	N	S	V
U	E	A	M	Z	O	V	S	N	Z
D	R	A	J	L	U	Z	H	O	S
S	S	L	F	E	J	D	I	W	O
W	W	J	H	A	I	L	N	Q	Z
S	T	O	R	M	W	K	E	O	D

SUNSHINE   MIST
CLOUDS   STORM
DRIZZLE   THUNDER
FOG   WIND
SNOW   HAIL

43

MAZE PUZZLE

Help the giraffe find a way to the tree!

SCRAMBLED WORDS

Unscramble the words, which are the names of the months.

CHAMR   _____

TUUSAG   _____

PRLIA   _____

YLJU   _____

JNEU   _____

UBRRYEFA   _____

AYM   _____

PRMEEBETS   _____

VNROEEBM   _____

BCOTORE   _____

FOLLOW THE PATTERNS

Color the shape that comes next.

BODY PARTS CROSSWORD

Complete the crossword puzzle by filling in the appropriate letters with the help of words listed below.

DOWN
1. T _ _ T _
2. H _ _ _
4. S _ _ M _ _ _
6. F _ _ _
7. _ _ S _

ACROSS
3. E _ _ S
5. _ O _ _ H
6. _ I _ _ _ R
8. _ R _
9. H _ _ R _

47

COLORING ADDITION

Find the sum for each addition problem. Use the sum to find the correct color listed below.

Orange = 11,12   Green = 16,20   Brown = 14

Blue = 9,13   Yellow = 10   Black = 8,18

HERO

Find the right suerhero shadows.

MATH SEARCH

Certain numbers in this puzzle, when added together,
will make a total that matches the given sum in the center.
The numbers must be connected horizontally, vertically or diagonally.
The connected numbers must be in one straight line.

1	9	4	8	5	1	5	1	7	8
4	5	3	3	2	5	6	9	4	2
8	2	4	3	1	5	3	9	8	1
2	2	2	4	7	4	7	8	7	2
5	1	5	4	**37**		7	7	4	8
7	3	6	8			8	9	5	1
2	1	9	3	1	2	6	9	3	1
9	4	4	8	3	2	6	8	3	4
6	6	7	2	6	4	7	5	3	3
9	5	3	3	4	4	7	4	9	4

You can find 13 ways
to make a sum of
37 in this puzzle.

(One of the 13 answers has
been done for you!)

You can find 13 ways
to make a sum of
36 in this puzzle.

(One of the 13 answers has
been done for you!)

8	2	3	2	7	9	5	5	6	1
2	8	1	5	8	5	4	8	8	7
2	6	2	5	6	7	7	7	7	1
3	2	8	4	3	8	1	9	5	3
5	9	8	1	**36**		8	2	3	1
7	5	5	8			4	4	7	6
9	9	6	1	7	6	1	2	3	3
5	4	6	3	7	3	4	9	4	2
5	1	8	5	3	7	2	1	1	3
2	7	5	8	3	6	1	9	9	2

FRUITS WORD SEARCH

Find all the hidden words that are listed below. Words can be up, down, forward, or diagonal.

I	A	E	K	F	O	R	A	N	G	E	Y	V
S	P	Y	B	A	N	A	N	A	P	L	U	M
B	I	N	S	T	R	A	W	B	E	R	R	Y
L	N	W	A	T	E	R	M	E	L	O	N	G
A	E	H	Z	P	U	T	M	E	L	O	N	L
C	A	T	A	V	O	C	A	D	O	O	C	C
K	P	H	I	S	I	P	T	B	X	W	S	G
B	P	K	I	W	I	U	E	Y	I	I	E	R
E	L	E	I	F	N	S	R	A	T	W	Q	A
R	E	T	H	O	N	R	Y	L	C	R	Z	P
R	L	L	C	P	E	L	C	E	Q	H	E	E
Y	N	O	O	H	A	P	R	I	C	O	T	S
G	C	Q	C	B	O	I	S	A	P	P	L	E

APPLE	CHERRY	ORANGE
APRICOT	COCONUT	PEACH
AVOCADO	GRAPES	STRAWBERRY
BANANA	KIWI	PLUM
BLACKBERRY	MELON	WATERMELON

52

MAZE PUZZLE

Help the fish find a way to the coral!

SCRAMBLED WORDS

Unscramble the words, which are shapes.

ASREQU   _____

ERCLIC   _____

GNRTIELA   _____

SART   _____

EXNGOHA   _____

GNOACTO   _____

COBUDI   _____

PESERH   _____

ECNO   _____

CINLREDY   _____

FOLLOW THE PATTERNS

Color the object that comes next.

FRUITS CROSSWORD

Complete the crossword puzzle by filling in the appropriate letters with the help of hints listed below.

ACROSS
3. Named after a brown bird
5. Big and green with stripes outside, but red inside
6. The fruit likes to hang around in bunches
8. One a day will keep the doctor away!

DOWN
1. Red and has seeds on the outside
2. Its color is the same as its name
4. Monkeys love to eat it
7. A fuzzy fruit

COLORING ADDITION

Find the sum for each addition problem. Use the sum to find the correct color listed below.

Red = 21   Green = 24   Orange = 17

Yellow = 15   Blue = 26   Pink = 19

PARTY

The shadows disappeared on the party. Help find them so they can share the gifts!

FIND 10 DIFFERENCES

MATH SEARCH

Certain numbers in this puzzle, when added together,
will make a total that matches the given sum in the center.
The numbers must be connected horizontally, vertically or diagonally.
The connected numbers must be in one straight line.

6	2	4	7	6	6	7	9	6	1
7	9	2	7	1	5	6	2	6	6
8	1	1	1	8	1	2	9	5	3
5	1	4	3	8	5	8	4	6	3
9	6	9	5	45		6	3	7	1
6	6	9	7			1	9	1	1
9	8	5	1	6	6	9	2	5	7
7	9	5	4	6	5	9	6	9	7
3	8	1	1	5	3	7	3	6	6
8	4	5	7	1	4	2	3	2	3

You can find 7 ways
to make a sum of
45 in this puzzle.

(One of the 7 answers has
been done for you!)

You can find 9 ways
to make a sum of
40 in this puzzle.

(One of the 9 answers has
been done for you!)

7	8	5	3	3	3	1	2	7	2
3	7	3	9	3	4	5	6	4	4
8	6	6	7	9	8	2	5	7	4
9	1	8	6	3	2	5	8	3	4
3	6	8	5	40		9	5	7	6
3	6	6	8			4	7	5	5
5	2	2	5	8	7	9	8	2	2
4	4	6	3	3	2	9	7	7	3
1	9	4	5	8	9	7	8	7	8
8	1	3	8	1	1	9	2	3	4

ANIMALS WORD SEARCH

Find all the hidden words that are listed below. Words can be up, down, forward, or diagonal.

R	P	P	S	P	M	O	N	K	E	Y	K	S
N	I	B	L	L	X	J	F	T	G	M	I	H
K	C	P	K	A	N	G	A	R	O	O	I	P
F	A	A	V	T	T	I	G	E	R	N	N	T
F	M	N	W	A	H	R	G	N	S	O	N	C
D	E	D	W	L	X	A	X	A	I	A	O	H
O	L	A	H	L	B	F	Y	L	H	E	M	I
N	X	S	A	I	Y	F	S	P	L	P	P	P
K	P	N	B	G	L	E	E	T	K	D	T	P
E	V	A	V	A	G	L	R	P	F	Y	J	O
Y	K	K	O	T	E	U	K	B	Q	J	A	D
P	O	E	F	O	T	D	A	A	T	Q	I	M
M	Z	E	B	R	A	K	O	A	L	A	H	T

MONKEY	ELEPHANT	KANGAROO
TIGER	ZEBRA	SNAKE
PANDA	GIRAFFE	ALLIGATOR
KOALA	CAMEL	TURTLE
LION	HIPPO	DONKEY

MAZE PUZZLE

Help her find a way to the chick!

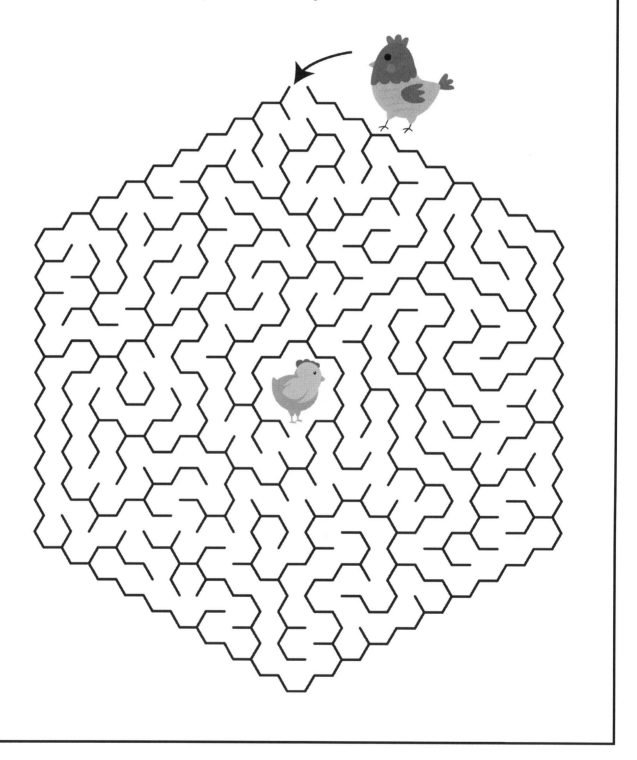

SCRAMBLED WORDS

Unscramble the words that are related to sports.

CNYCILG   _____

NINCFGE   _____

TAOOFBLL   _____

TINENS   _____

LOGF   _____

HEYKOC   _____

RYHRAEC   _____

TABODINMN   _____

LALBBASE   _____

BEALBSKTAL   _____

FOLLOW THE PATTERNS

Color the farm animal that comes next.

CAMPING CROSSWORD

Complete the crossword puzzle by filling in the appropriate letters with the help of words listed below.

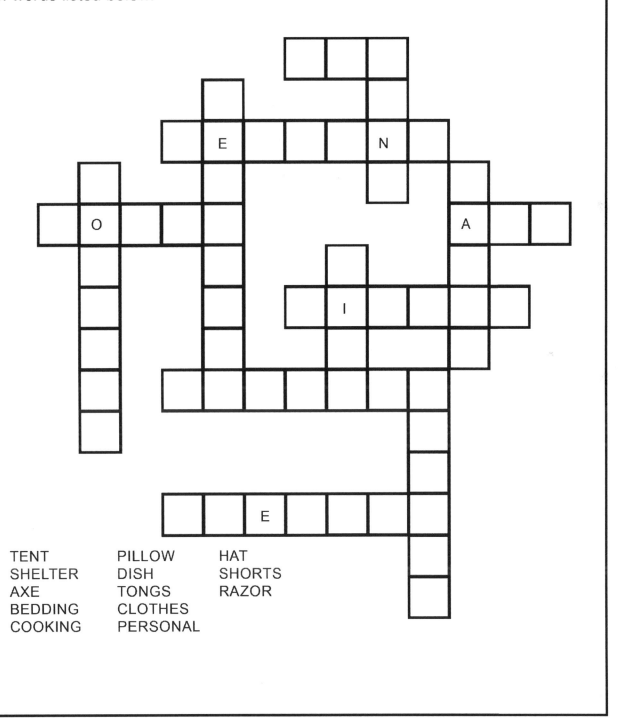

TENT	PILLOW	HAT
SHELTER	DISH	SHORTS
AXE	TONGS	RAZOR
BEDDING	CLOTHES	
COOKING	PERSONAL	

COLORING ADDITION

Find the sum for each addition problem. Use the sum to find the correct color listed below.

Blue = 18,23   Green = 28,30   Red = 19   Orange = 24

Brown = 15   Black = 26   Pink = 14,17   Yellow = 21,25

FARM

Help the farmer to find the right shadows,
so he can bring the animals into the barn.

MATH SEARCH

Certain numbers in this puzzle, when added together,
will make a total that matches the given sum in the center.
The numbers must be connected horizontally, vertically or diagonally.
The connected numbers must be in one straight line.

6	(7	3	4	9	4	7	2	3)	4
9	4	5	9	9	3	8	4	4	6
8	8	2	1	7	5	3	4	7	8
5	3	2	4	3	4	9	6	9	2
8	9	5	9	**39**		8	9	8	6
4	1	6	3			3	6	6	1
8	9	9	1	9	7	7	9	8	2
8	9	6	1	2	7	9	3	9	2
3	7	3	1	8	4	2	9	4	9
2	2	7	8	7	6	6	2	6	4

You can find 8 ways
to make a sum of
39 in this puzzle.

(One of the 8 answers has
been done for you!)

You can find 10 ways
to make a sum of
49 in this puzzle.

(One of the 10 answers has
been done for you!)

5	4	8	(7	8	5	9	6	1	4	9)	9
9	5	4	5	8	5	9	6	2	6	1	2
5	7	5	6	8	8	5	3	5	3	6	1
4	7	4	3	5	5	3	4	6	3	2	3
4	9	2	7	2	8	1	2	7	2	1	8
1	7	5	3	4	**49**		1	4	4	9	1
9	3	2	3	2			6	1	6	9	2
7	3	3	2	6	3	7	9	5	4	1	4
1	8	6	3	5	5	2	7	1	9	7	2
8	2	7	1	8	5	4	3	4	7	8	6
5	9	7	2	7	6	8	6	9	5	3	1
9	1	3	6	3	8	4	3	6	4	8	5

INSTRUMENTS WORD SEARCH

Find all the hidden words that are listed below. Words can be up, down, forward, or diagonal.

H	A	R	P	E	B	P	U	D	I	D	C	S
Y	P	V	L	X	T	A	N	M	R	S	T	I
S	U	G	E	R	Y	R	N	Y	S	U	D	N
U	U	V	H	W	Q	L	U	J	I	L	M	C
B	W	H	P	I	A	N	O	M	O	H	J	L
F	L	U	T	E	M	B	W	P	P	C	M	A
P	I	C	C	C	R	C	O	R	H	E	G	R
F	R	N	C	H	H	O	R	N	H	O	T	I
H	X	S	A	X	O	P	H	O	N	E	N	N
C	E	L	L	O	Z	N	S	C	C	W	A	E
I	P	V	G	T	R	O	M	B	O	N	E	T
K	I	K	G	U	I	T	A	R	E	H	S	A
H	A	R	M	O	N	I	C	A	Q	L	T	C

PIANO	BANJO	SAXOPHONE
HARP	TROMBONE	BUGLE
DRUM	TRUMPET	HARMONICA
CLARINET	XYLOPHONE	FLUTE
GUITAR	CELLO	

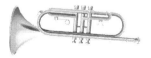

MAZE PUZZLE

Help the rabbit find a way to the carrots!

SCRAMBLED WORDS

Unscramble the words, which are the names of colors.

BELU   _____

KCLBA   _____

OBNWR   _____

NEREG   _____

RAEGON   _____

ULEPRP   _____

IPNK   _____

THEIW   _____

ELYLOW   _____

RVLESI   _____

FOLLOW THE PATTERNS

Color the insect that comes next.

SEA ANIMALS CROSSWORD

Complete the crossword puzzle by filling in the appropriate letters with the help of pictures.

DOWN

2
4
6
7
9

ACROSS

1
10
3
5
8

COLORING ADDITION

Find the sum for each addition problem. Use the sum to find the correct color listed below.

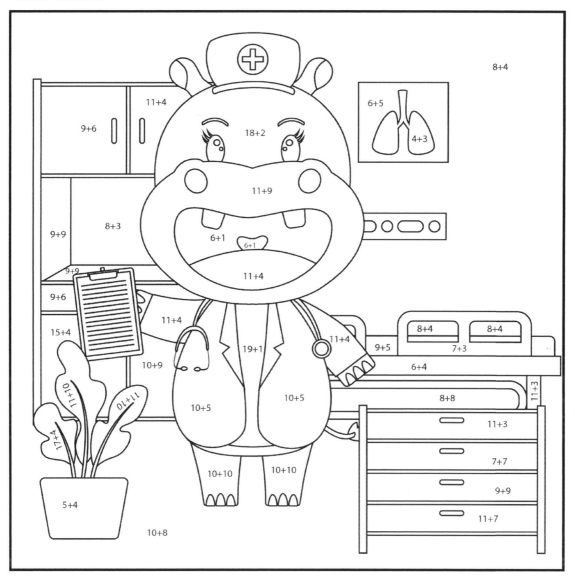

Orange = 9,11   Blue = 12,16   Red = 7   Brown = 14,18

Green = 21   Pink = 15,19   Yellow = 10   Gray = 20

TOYS

The toys are sad without their shadows. Find the right shadows to make them happy.

FIND 10 DIFFERENCES

MATH SEARCH

Certain numbers in this puzzle, when added together,
will make a total that matches the given sum in the center.
The numbers must be connected horizontally, vertically or diagonally.
The connected numbers must be in one straight line.

3	1	7	6	2	3	9	3	8	8	3	6
1	7	3	5	8	8	3	7	6	6	3	4
7	8	4	3	5	1	9	9	5	7	1	6
2	5	7	4	5	1	5	6	2	6	5	3
7	1	4	7	2	9	2	4	2	2	5	1
9	6	6	7	4	**52**		1	8	8	1	8
6	3	1	1	4			1	5	3	7	4
7	5	5	4	7	6	7	5	6	8	2	4
8	5	3	1	1	9	8	5	8	5	9	9
7	6	9	1	1	1	8	8	4	7	7	7
8	4	3	9	1	6	7	2	1	2	5	2
3	8	6	6	2	4	2	7	6	8	1	1

You can find 9 ways
to make a sum of
52 in this puzzle.

(One of the 9 answers has
been done for you!)

You can find 15 ways
to make a sum of
47 in this puzzle.

(One of the 15 answers has
been done for you!)

3	8	6	4	1	7	3	2	7	4	2	2
3	4	2	8	2	3	2	4	5	1	7	6
7	8	3	5	6	5	3	4	6	7	9	7
4	8	3	4	2	1	6	8	2	5	2	7
1	5	9	7	6	2	8	4	6	4	9	8
5	7	7	3	1	**47**		6	1	1	2	9
5	4	4	2	6			1	5	6	5	9
4	6	1	8	6	9	7	3	1	2	1	8
9	3	5	5	2	3	6	4	6	1	4	6
9	7	6	3	3	6	9	7	4	2	1	2
1	5	9	8	9	6	5	9	5	4	7	9
3	9	6	1	9	4	5	3	9	9	3	5

OCCUPATIONS WORD SEARCH

Find all the hidden words that are listed below. Words can be up, down, forward, or diagonal.

Y	A	A	C	X	S	A	V	P	A	I	N	T	E	R
A	A	R	T	I	S	T	P	X	S	P	R	Y	U	E
G	R	D	W	L	R	J	O	M	G	I	I	H	D	W
D	O	T	D	Y	N	Q	L	J	B	S	N	H	U	A
U	O	M	U	S	I	C	I	A	N	D	G	G	T	E
A	G	L	R	W	W	O	C	C	U	M	E	O	E	J
G	Q	C	D	R	I	V	E	R	V	V	L	N	K	R
G	T	L	P	I	L	J	M	J	D	I	R	F	B	D
J	F	A	R	M	E	R	A	Y	P	H	R	I	U	D
D	W	I	J	E	N	D	N	N	U	O	S	R	T	Z
O	D	R	E	F	C	O	O	X	L	O	S	E	C	N
C	D	Y	H	O	K	P	B	I	T	V	G	M	H	H
T	E	A	C	H	E	R	A	C	G	L	M	A	E	L
O	H	D	D	E	N	T	I	S	T	S	J	N	R	T
R	V	G	A	L	G	P	G	C	O	O	K	W	K	V

PILOT
POLICEMAN
DOCTOR
ARTIST
SINGER

TEACHER
COOK
DENTIST
MUSICIAN
PAINTER

DRIVER
FIREMAN
BUTCHER
FARMER
TAILOR

79

MAZE PUZZLE

Help the spider find a way to the web!

SCRAMBLED WORDS

Unscramble the words which are related to stationery.

LRERU   _____

KBOO   _____

ELRASTP   _____

IPCL   _____

RTECUT   _____

IGWDARN   _____

CLPENI   _____

EAESRR   _____

UELG   _____

KNDPIA   _____

FOLLOW THE PATTERNS

Color the easter egg that comes next.

ANIMALS WORD SEARCH

Complete the crossword puzzle by filling in the appropriate letters with the help of hints listed below.

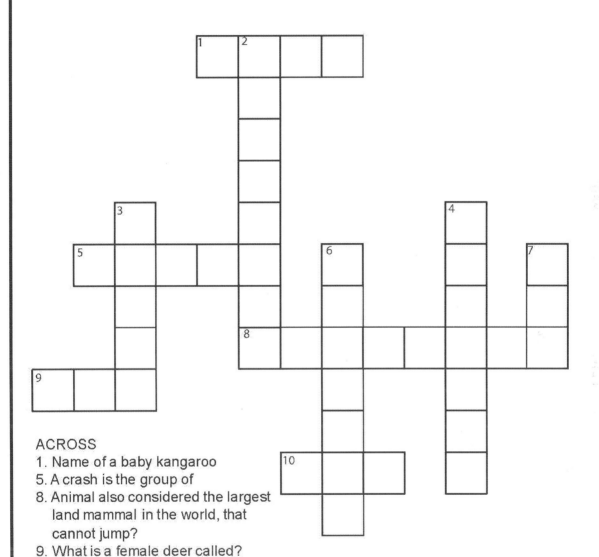

ACROSS
1. Name of a baby kangaroo
5. A crash is the group of
8. Animal also considered the largest land mammal in the world, that cannot jump?
9. What is a female deer called?
10. Which mammal can truly fly?

DOWN
2. What is the animal called that eats both plant and meat?
3. Which is the largest mammal in the ocean?
4. Which is the tallest animal?
6. What is the fastest land animal?
7. What animal is said to have 9 lives?

COLORING ADDITION

Find the sum for each addition problem. Use the sum to find the correct color listed below.

Brown = 21   Yellow = 26   Green = 19   Red = 23

Blue = 17,25   Purple = 11   Pink = 9,15   Orange = 13,28

84

SEA ANIMALS

You are on a journey to the depths of the ocean.
Try to find the right shadows.

FIND 10 DIFFERENCES

MATH SEARCH

Certain numbers in this puzzle, when added together,
will make a total that matches the given sum in the center.
The numbers must be connected horizontally, vertically or diagonally.
The connected numbers must be in one straight line.

1	4	7	6	4	4	5	6	2	4	2	7
7	5	6	1	8	5	1	9	1	8	7	1
7	8	4	9	6	9	2	7	6	3	1	2
6	3	7	9	6	4	7	8	9	2	9	6
6	6	6	2	4	4	4	9	7	9	1	8
7	9	7	2	3	**51**	3	5	9	2	7
1	4	6	8	8		7	8	6	2	2
2	5	6	4	2	8	5	9	5	4	5	6
3	2	5	7	7	2	7	5	6	5	5	2
2	2	6	8	1	8	4	5	3	2	1	1
1	8	5	4	5	3	4	1	9	9	8	6
7	5	8	1	6	2	4	3	7	7	7	4

You can find 10 ways
to make a sum of
51 in this puzzle.

(One of the 10 answers has
been done for you!)

You can find 9 ways
to make a sum of
48 in this puzzle.

(One of the 9 answers has
been done for you!)

2	2	4	4	9	8	2	1	7	5	6	7
9	6	1	7	7	1	2	8	4	1	8	2
7	8	3	9	1	6	3	5	8	8	1	3
3	7	3	6	3	5	5	4	8	9	7	9
7	5	8	9	5	2	7	7	3	2	1	7
8	4	7	8	6	**48**	8	1	3	5	5
5	9	8	8	1		1	8	2	5	8
8	6	2	3	1	6	8	5	1	1	5	3
4	8	2	9	1	2	5	9	4	5	1	3
7	7	6	8	9	8	9	3	1	3	2	7
8	2	1	8	1	6	5	5	9	6	6	1
1	8	7	1	6	6	3	9	3	7	8	6

EMOTIONS WORD SEARCH

Find all the hidden words that are listed below. Words can be up, down, forward, or diagonal.

```
C  S  A  P  R  O  U  D  O  J  F  O  S  S  L
B  R  X  W  K  G  T  Z  T  J  N  D  I  S  U
Z  O  Q  S  L  W  D  K  X  I  E  R  L  C  X
S  U  R  P  R  I  S  E  D  K  R  J  L  A  A
X  B  T  E  E  Z  R  F  F  H  V  E  Y  R  N
R  K  H  T  D  Q  W  U  L  O  O  P  D  E  G
E  S  E  X  C  I  T  E  D  Z  U  J  S  D  R
N  D  I  A  F  O  Y  W  N  B  S  Z  A  W  Y
T  E  X  J  D  T  H  A  P  P  Y  W  D  C  M
P  H  I  E  M  B  A  R  R  A  S  S  E  D  K
C  O  N  F  U  S  E  D  Y  A  J  V  G  E  D
G  S  J  K  R  I  J  P  G  X  C  Y  V  W  Y
F  A  S  S  U  S  P  I  C  I  O  U  S  M  X
E  T  W  O  R  R  I  E  D  P  F  E  Y  S  Z
S  B  R  S  E  S  Z  W  J  H  O  O  Z  Q  A
```

ANGRY
BORED
CONFUSED
EMBARRASSED
EXCITED

HAPPY
NERVOUS
PROUD
SAD
SCARED

SILLY
SURPRISED
SUSPICIOUS
TIRED
WORRIED

SCRAMBLED WORDS

Unscramble the words, which are animals.

TKINET   _____

EOMYNK   _____

USEOM   _____

GREIT   _____

EBRA   _____

FLOBUAF   _____

LAFC   _____

ALMCE   _____

RBEZA   _____

EERD   _____

FOLLOW THE PATTERNS

Color the donut that comes next.

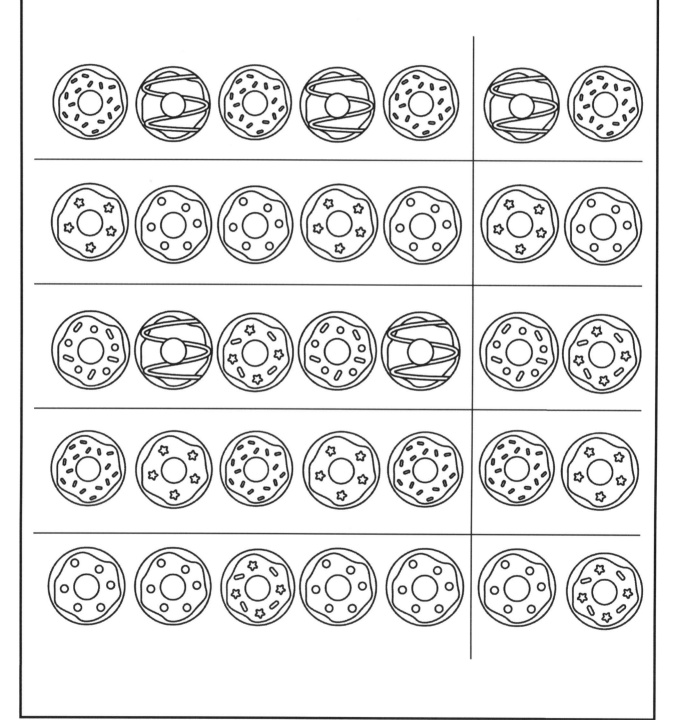

90

COLORING ADDITION

Find the sum for each addition problem. Use the sum to find the correct color listed below.

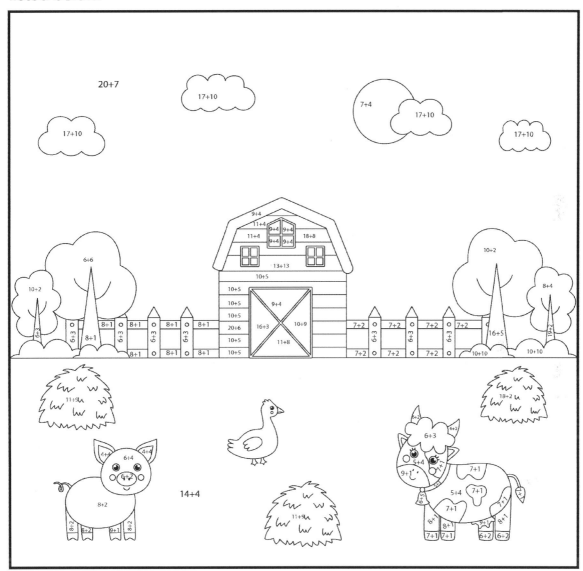

Blue = 27   Brown = 9,18,21   Red = 15,26   Yellow = 11

Orange = 13,19   Green = 12,20   Black = 8   Pink = 10

BIRDS CROSSWORD

Complete the crossword puzzle by filling in the appropriate letters with the help of pictures given below.

Answer Key

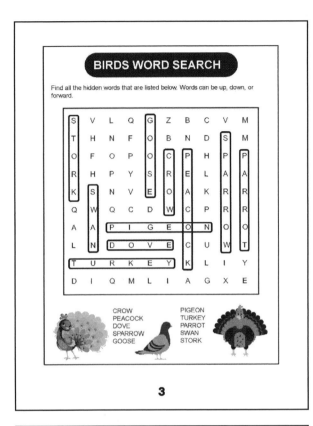

BIRDS WORD SEARCH

Find all the hidden words that are listed below. Words can be up, down, or forward.

CROW
PEACOCK
DOVE
SPARROW
GOOSE

PIGEON
TURKEY
PARROT
SWAN
STORK

3

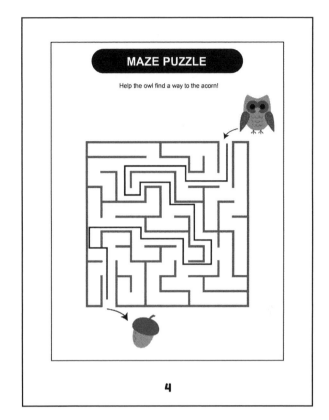

MAZE PUZZLE

Help the owl find a way to the acorn!

4

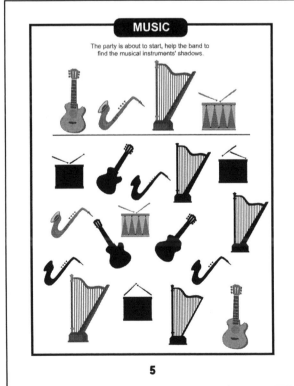

MUSIC

The party is about to start, help the band to find the musical instruments' shadows.

5

FIND 10 DIFFERENCES

6

93

Answer Key

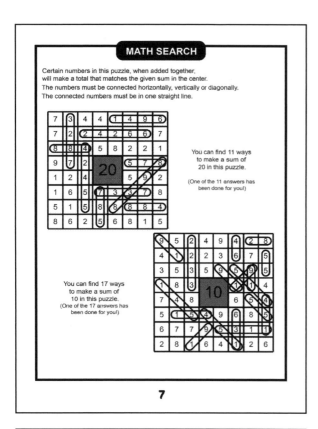

MATH SEARCH

Certain numbers in this puzzle, when added together,
will make a total that matches the given sum in the center.
The numbers must be connected horizontally, vertically or diagonally.
The connected numbers must be in one straight line.

You can find 11 ways
to make a sum of
20 in this puzzle.

(One of the 11 answers has
been done for you!)

You can find 17 ways
to make a sum of
10 in this puzzle.
(One of the 17 answers has
been done for you!)

7

MAZE PUZZLE

Help the lion find a way the cub!

8

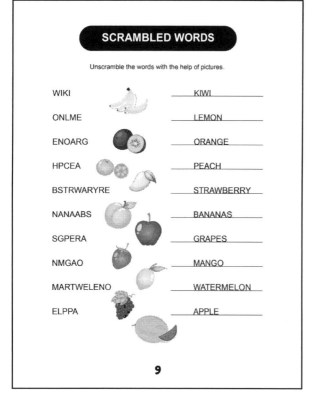

SCRAMBLED WORDS

Unscramble the words with the help of pictures.

WIKI — KIWI

ONLME — LEMON

ENOARG — ORANGE

HPCEA — PEACH

BSTRWARYRE — STRAWBERRY

NANAABS — BANANAS

SGPERA — GRAPES

NMGAO — MANGO

MARTWELENO — WATERMELON

ELPPA — APPLE

9

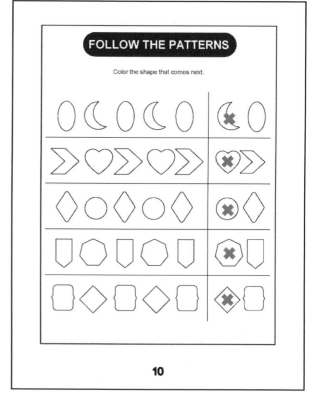

FOLLOW THE PATTERNS

Color the shape that comes next.

10

Answer Key

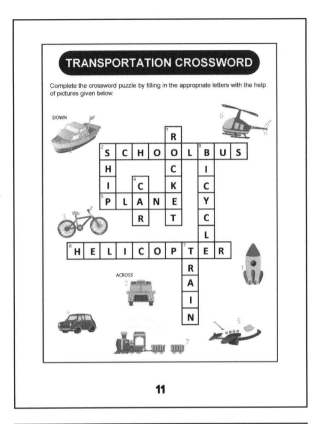

TRANSPORTATION CROSSWORD

Complete the crossword puzzle by filling in the appropriate letters with the help of pictures given below.

SCHOOL

Help the students to find the shadows.

11

13

FIND 10 DIFFERENCES

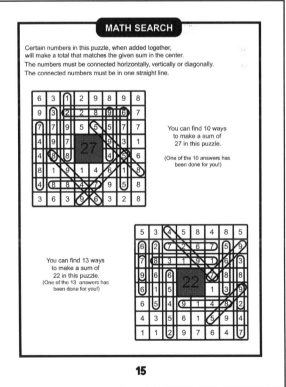

MATH SEARCH

Certain numbers in this puzzle, when added together, will make a total that matches the given sum in the center. The numbers must be connected horizontally, vertically or diagonally. The connected numbers must be in one straight line.

You can find 10 ways to make a sum of 27 in this puzzle.

(One of the 10 answers has been done for you!)

You can find 13 ways to make a sum of 22 in this puzzle.
(One of the 13 answers has been done for you!)

14

15

95

Answer Key

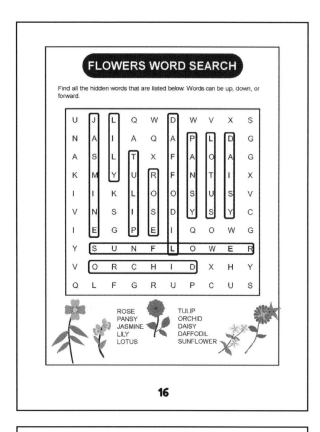

FLOWERS WORD SEARCH

Find all the hidden words that are listed below. Words can be up, down, or forward.

U	J	L	Q	W	D	W	V	X	S
N	A	I	A	Q	A	P	L	D	G
A	S	L	T	X	F	A	O	A	G
K	M	Y	U	R	F	N	T	I	X
V	I	K	L	O	O	S	U	S	V
I	N	S	I	S	D	Y	S	Y	C
Y	E	G	P	E	I	Q	O	W	G
Y		S	U	N	F	L	O	W	E	R
V		O	R	C	H	I	D	X	H	Y
Q	L	F	G	R	U	P	C	U	S

ROSE
PANSY
JASMINE
LILY
LOTUS

TULIP
ORCHID
DAISY
DAFFODIL
SUNFLOWER

16

MAZE PUZZLE

Help the monkey find a way to the bananas!

17

SCRAMBLED WORDS

Unscramble the spelling words with the help of pictures.

RTEE — TREE

ITUGAR — GUITAR

SNU — SUN

EBTCUK — BUCKET

CIRHA — CHAIR

PLIECN — PENCIL

ARCMIECE — ICECREAM

CNDYA — CANDY

LALB — BALL

EBLMRULA — UMBRELLA

18

FOLLOW THE PATTERNS

Color the butterfly that comes next.

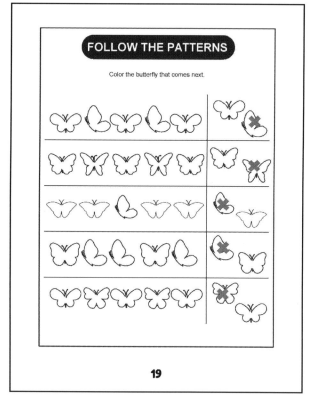

19

Answer Key

CROSSWORD PUZZLE

Complete the crossword puzzle by filling in the appropriate letters with the help of words listed below.

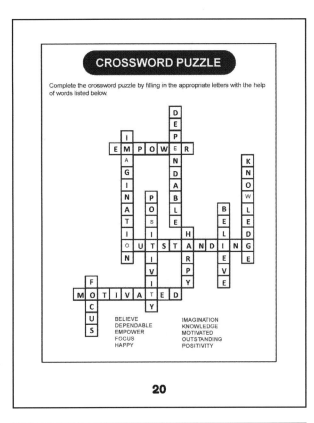

BELIEVE
DEPENDABLE
EMPOWER
FOCUS
HAPPY

IMAGINATION
KNOWLEDGE
MOTIVATED
OUTSTANDING
POSITIVITY

20

ZOO

Welcome to the zoo! Try to find the shadows.

22

FIND 10 DIFFERENCES

23

MATH SEARCH

Certain numbers in this puzzle, when added together, will make a total that matches the given sum in the center.
The numbers must be connected horizontally, vertically or diagonally.
The connected numbers must be in one straight line.

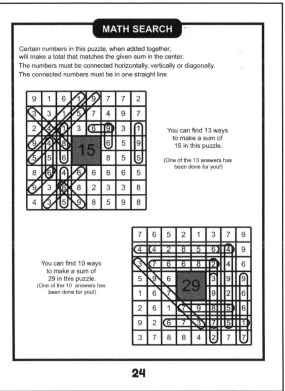

You can find 13 ways to make a sum of 15 in this puzzle.

(One of the 13 answers has been done for you!)

You can find 10 ways to make a sum of 29 in this puzzle.
(One of the 10 answers has been done for you!)

24

Answer Key

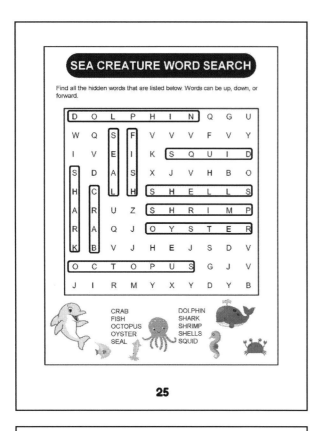

SEA CREATURE WORD SEARCH

Find all the hidden words that are listed below. Words can be up, down, or forward.

D	O	L	P	H	I	N	Q	G	U
W	Q	S	F	V	V	V	F	V	Y
I	V	E	I	K	S	Q	U	I	D
S	D	A	S	X	J	V	H	B	O
H	C	L	H	S	H	E	L	L	S
A	R	U	Z	S	H	R	I	M	P
R	A	Q	J	O	Y	S	T	E	R
K	B	V	J	H	E	J	S	D	V
O	C	T	O	P	U	S	G	J	V
J	I	R	M	Y	X	Y	D	Y	B

CRAB
FISH
OCTOPUS
OYSTER
SEAL

DOLPHIN
SHARK
SHRIMP
SHELLS
SQUID

25

MAZE PUZZLE

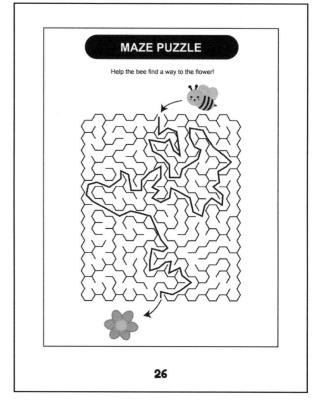

Help the bee find a way to the flower!

26

SCRAMBLED WORDS

Unscramble the spelling words that are colors name.

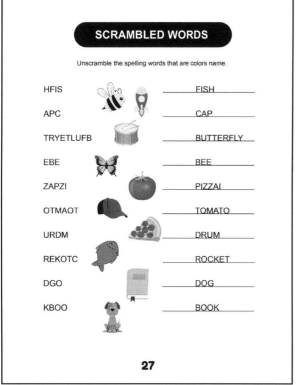

HFIS	FISH
APC	CAP
TRYETLUFB	BUTTERFLY
EBE	BEE
ZAPZI	PIZZAI
OTMAOT	TOMATO
URDM	DRUM
REKOTC	ROCKET
DGO	DOG
KBOO	BOOK

27

FOLLOW THE PATTERNS

Color the flower that comes next.

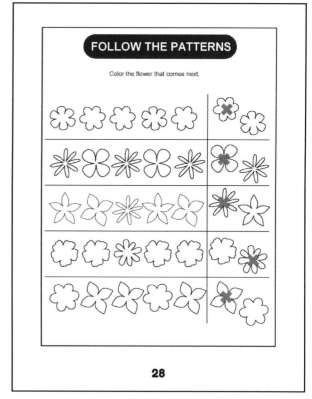

28

Answer Key

CROSSWORD PUZZLE

Complete the crossword puzzle by filling in the appropriate letters with the help of words listed below.

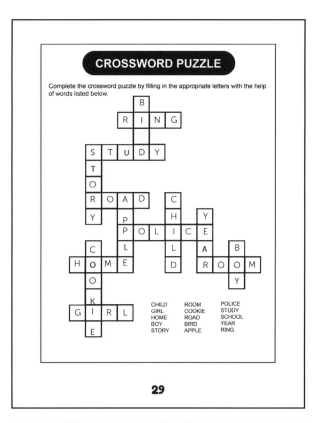

CHILD	ROOM	POLICE
GIRL	COOKIE	STUDY
HOME	ROAD	SCHOOL
BOY	BIRD	YEAR
STORY	APPLE	RING

29

DINOSAUR

We are back to the cretaceous period.
Try to find the dinosaurs' shadows.

31

FIND 10 DIFFERENCES

32

MATH SEARCH

Certain numbers in this puzzle, when added together, will make a total that matches the given sum in the center.
The numbers must be connected horizontally, vertically or diagonally.
The connected numbers must be in one straight line.

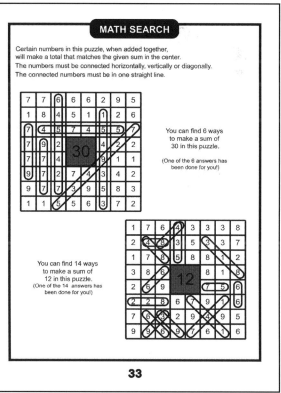

You can find 6 ways to make a sum of 30 in this puzzle.

(One of the 6 answers has been done for you!)

You can find 14 ways to make a sum of 12 in this puzzle.
(One of the 14 answers has been done for you!)

33

Answer Key

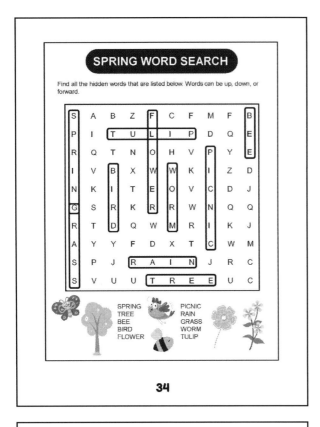

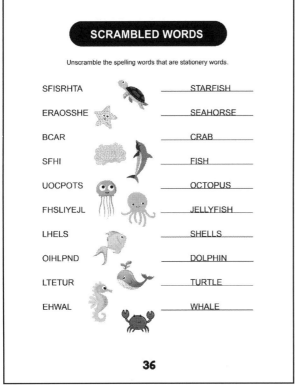

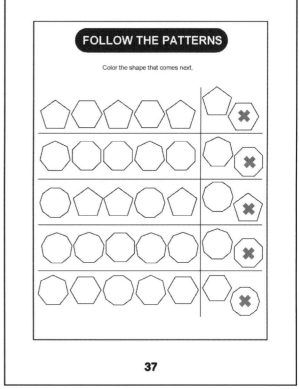

34

35

36

37

100

Answer Key

SPACE

Let's take a trip to space. Try to find the right shadows.

40

FIND 10 DIFFERENCES

41

MATH SEARCH

Certain numbers in this puzzle, when added together, will make a total that matches the given sum in the center. The numbers must be connected horizontally, vertically or diagonally. The connected numbers must be in one straight line.

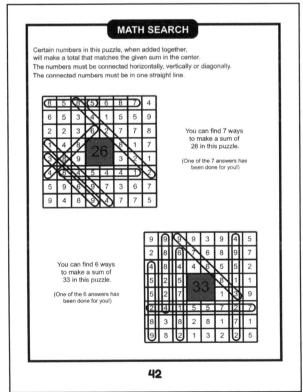

You can find 7 ways to make a sum of 26 in this puzzle.

(One of the 7 answers has been done for you!)

You can find 6 ways to make a sum of 33 in this puzzle.

(One of the 6 answers has been done for you!)

42

WEATHER WORD SEARCH

Find all the hidden words that are listed below. Words can be up, down, or forward.

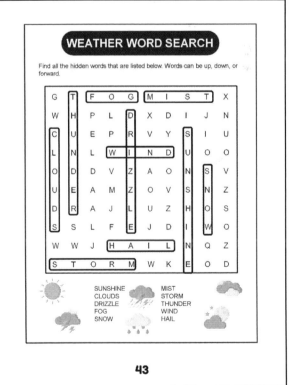

SUNSHINE
CLOUDS
DRIZZLE
FOG
SNOW

MIST
STORM
THUNDER
WIND
HAIL

43

Answer Key

MAZE PUZZLE

Help the giraffe find a way to the tree!

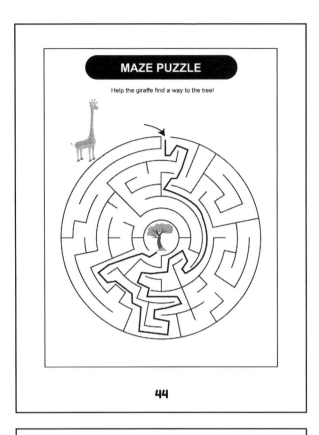

44

SCRAMBLED WORDS

Unscramble the spelling words that are months name.

CHAMR	MARCH
TUUSAG	AUGUST
PRLIA	APRIL
YLJU	JULY
JNEU	JUNE
UBRRYEFA	FEBRUARY
AYM	MAY
PRMEEBETS	SEPTEMBER
VNROEEBM	NOVEMBER
BCOTORE	OCTOBER

45

FOLLOW THE PATTERNS

Color the shape that comes next.

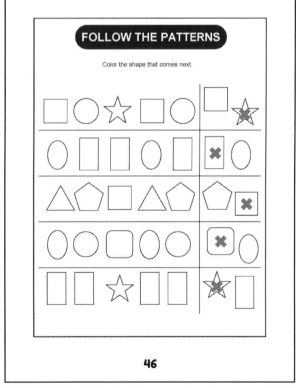

46

BODY PARTS CROSSWORD

Complete the crossword puzzle by filling in the appropriate letters with the help of words listed below.

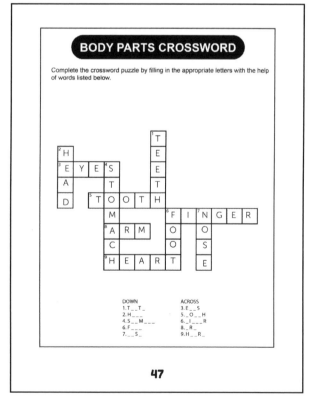

DOWN
1. T _ _ T _
2. H _ _ _
4. S _ _ M _ _ _
6. F _ _ _
7. _ _ S _

ACROSS
3. E _ _ S
5. _ O _ _ H
6. _ I _ _ _ R
8. _ R _
9. H _ _ R _

47

102

Answer Key

HERO

Find the right superhero shadows.

49

FIND 10 DIFFERENCES

50

MATH SEARCH

Certain numbers in this puzzle, when added together,
will make a total that matches the given sum in the center.
The numbers must be connected horizontally, vertically or diagonally.
The connected numbers must be in one straight line.

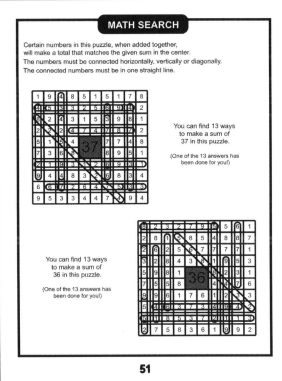

You can find 13 ways
to make a sum of
37 in this puzzle.

(One of the 13 answers has
been done for you!)

You can find 13 ways
to make a sum of
36 in this puzzle.

(One of the 13 answers has
been done for you!)

51

FRUITS WORD SEARCH

Find all the hidden words that are listed below. Words can be up, down, forward,
or diagonal.

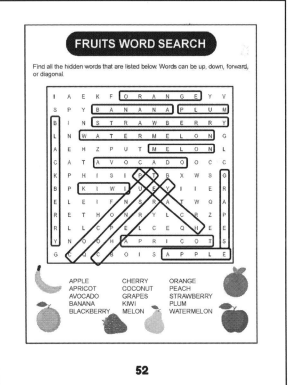

APPLE	CHERRY	ORANGE
APRICOT	COCONUT	PEACH
AVOCADO	GRAPES	STRAWBERRY
BANANA	KIWI	PLUM
BLACKBERRY	MELON	WATERMELON

52

103

Answer Key

MAZE PUZZLE

Help the fish find a way to the coral!

53

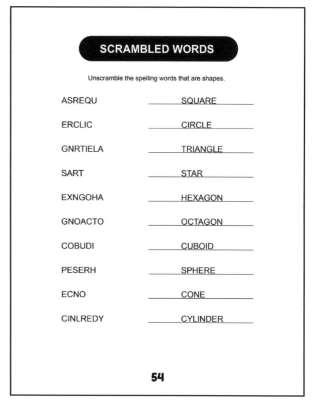

SCRAMBLED WORDS

Unscramble the spelling words that are shapes.

ASREQU	SQUARE
ERCLIC	CIRCLE
GNRTIELA	TRIANGLE
SART	STAR
EXNGOHA	HEXAGON
GNOACTO	OCTAGON
COBUDI	CUBOID
PESERH	SPHERE
ECNO	CONE
CINLREDY	CYLINDER

54

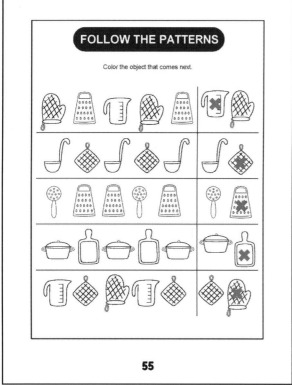

FOLLOW THE PATTERNS

Color the object that comes next.

55

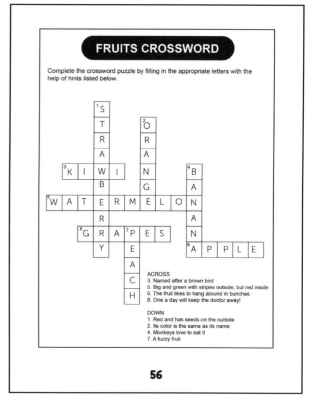

FRUITS CROSSWORD

Complete the crossword puzzle by filling in the appropriate letters with the help of hints listed below.

ACROSS
3. Named after a brown bird
5. Big and green with stripes outside, but red inside
6. The fruit likes to hang around in bunches
8. One a day will keep the doctor away!

DOWN
1. Red and has seeds on the outside
2. Its color is the same as its name
4. Monkeys love to eat it
7. A fuzzy fruit

56

Answer Key

PARTY

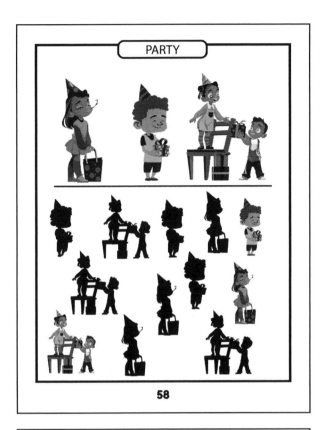

58

FIND 10 DIFFERENCES

59

MATH SEARCH

Certain numbers in this puzzle, when added together,
will make a total that matches the given sum in the center.
The numbers must be connected horizontally, vertically or diagonally.
The connected numbers must be in one straight line.

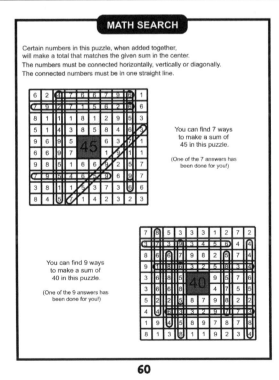

You can find 7 ways
to make a sum of
45 in this puzzle.

(One of the 7 answers has
been done for you!)

You can find 9 ways
to make a sum of
40 in this puzzle.

(One of the 9 answers has
been done for you!)

60

ANIMALS WORD SEARCH

Find all the hidden words that are listed below. Words can be up, down, forward,
or diagonal.

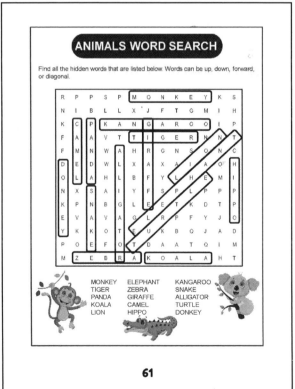

MONKEY	ELEPHANT	KANGAROO
TIGER	ZEBRA	SNAKE
PANDA	GIRAFFE	ALLIGATOR
KOALA	CAMEL	TURTLE
LION	HIPPO	DONKEY

61

Answer Key

MAZE PUZZLE

Help her find a way to the chick!

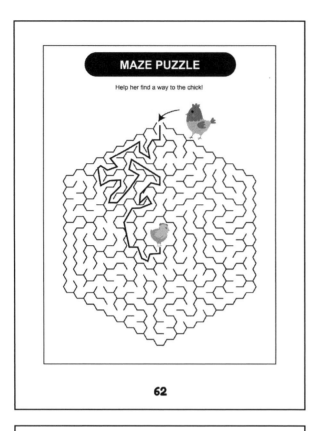

62

SCRAMBLED WORDS

Unscramble the words that are related to sports.

CNYCILG	CYCLING
NINCFGE	FENCING
TAOOFBLL	FOOTBALLL
TINENS	TENNIS
LOGF	GOLF
HEYKOC	HOCKEY
RYHRAEC	ARCHERY
TABODINMN	BADMINTON
LALBBASE	BASEBALL
BEALBSKTAL	BASKETBALL

63

FOLLOW THE PATTERNS

Color the farm animal that comes next.

64

CAMPING CROSSWORD

Complete the crossword puzzle by filling in the appropriate letters with the help of words listed below.

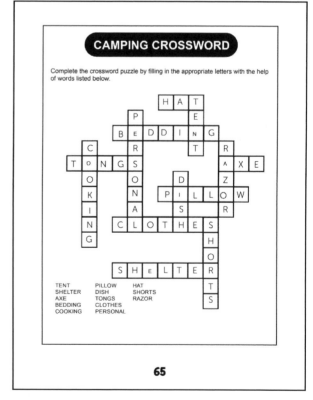

TENT   PILLOW   HAT
SHELTER   DISH   SHORTS
AXE   TONGS   RAZOR
BEDDING   CLOTHES
COOKING   PERSONAL

65

Answer Key

FARM

Help the farmer to find the right shadows, so he can bring the animals into the barn.

67

FIND 10 DIFFERENCES

68

MATH-SEARCH

Some numbers in this puzzle will make a total of the given when you add them up. The numbers must be connected horizontally, vertically or diagonally. The connected numbers must be in one straight line.

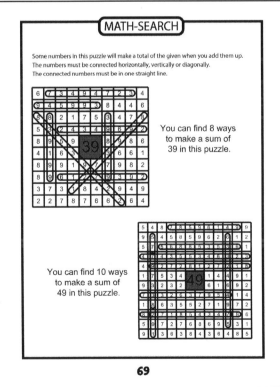

You can find 8 ways to make a sum of 39 in this puzzle.

You can find 10 ways to make a sum of 49 in this puzzle.

69

INSTRUMENTS WORD SEARCH

Find all the hidden words that are listed below. Words can be up, down, forward, or diagonal.

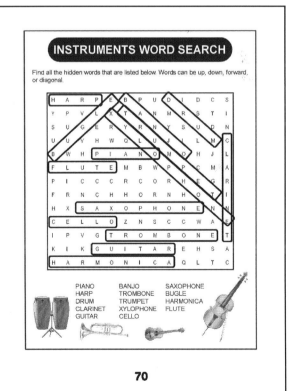

PIANO   BANJO   SAXOPHONE
HARP   TROMBONE   BUGLE
DRUM   TRUMPET   HARMONICA
CLARINET XYLOPHONE   FLUTE
GUITAR   CELLO

70

Answer Key

MAZE PUZZLE

Help the rabbit find a way to the carrots!

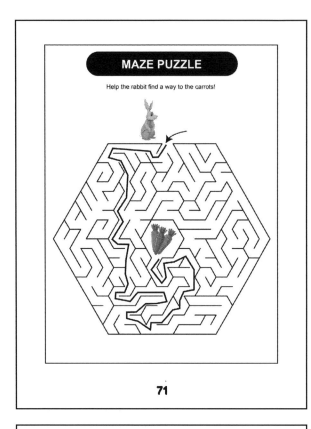

71

SCRAMBLED WORDS

Unscramble the spelling words that are colors name.

BELU	BLUE
KCLBA	BLACK
OBNWR	BROWN
NEREG	GREEN
RAEGON	ORANGE
ULEPRP	PURPLE
IPNK	PINK
THEIW	WHITE
ELYLOW	YELLOW
RVLESI	SILVER

72

FOLLOW THE PATTERNS

Color the insect that comes next.

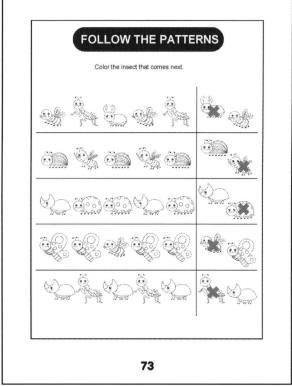

73

SEA ANIMALS CROSSWORD

Complete the crossword puzzle by filling in the appropriate letters with the help of pictures.

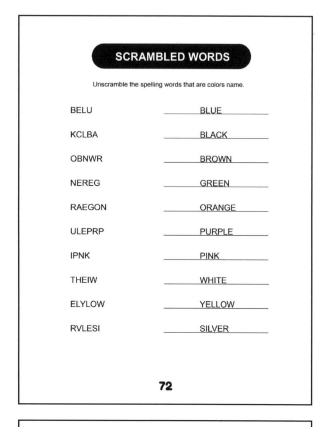

74

Answer Key

TOYS

The toys are sad without their shadows. Find the right shadows to make them happy.

76

FIND 10 DIFFERENCES

77

MATH SEARCH

Certain numbers in this puzzle, when added together, will make a total that matches the given sum in the center. The numbers must be connected horizontally, vertically or diagonally. The connected numbers must be in one straight line.

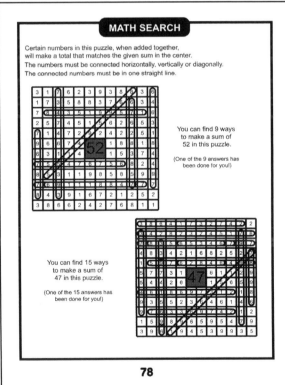

You can find 9 ways to make a sum of 52 in this puzzle.

(One of the 9 answers has been done for you!)

You can find 15 ways to make a sum of 47 in this puzzle.

(One of the 15 answers has been done for you!)

78

OCCUPATIONS WORD SEARCH

Find all the hidden words that are listed below. Words can be up, down, forward, or diagonal.

PILOT
POLICEMAN
DOCTOR
ARTIST
SINGER

TEACHER
COOK
DENTIST
MUSICIAN
PAINTER

DRIVER
FIREMAN
BUTCHER
FARMER
TAILOR

79

Answer Key

MAZE PUZZLE

Help the spider find a way to the web!

80

SCRAMBLED WORDS

Unscramble the spelling words that are stationery words.

LRERU	RULER
KBOO	BOOK
ELRASTP	STAPLER
IPCL	CLIPL
RTECUT	CUTTER
IGWDARN	DRAWING
CLPENI	PENCIL
EAESRR	ERASER
UELG	GLUE
KNDPIA	INKPAD

81

FOLLOW THE PATTERNS

Color the easter egg that comes next.

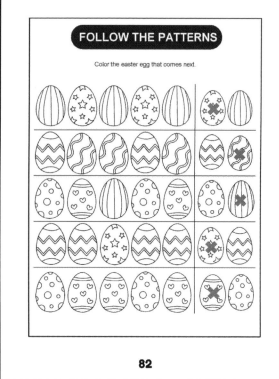

82

ANIMALS WORD SEARCH

Complete the crossword puzzle by filling in the appropriate letters with the help of hints listed below.

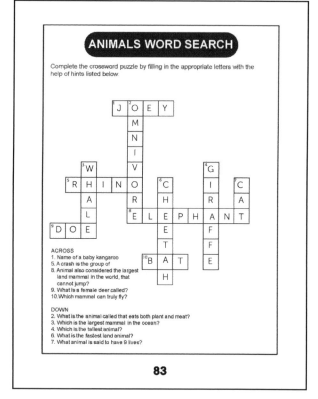

ACROSS
1. Name of a baby kangaroo
5. A crash is the group of
8. Animal also considered the largest land mammal in the world, that cannot jump?
9. What is a female deer called?
10. Which mammal can truly fly?

DOWN
2. What is the animal called that eats both plant and meat?
3. Which is the largest mammal in the ocean?
4. Which is the tallest animal?
6. What is the fastest land animal?
7. What animal is said to have 9 lives?

83

Answer Key

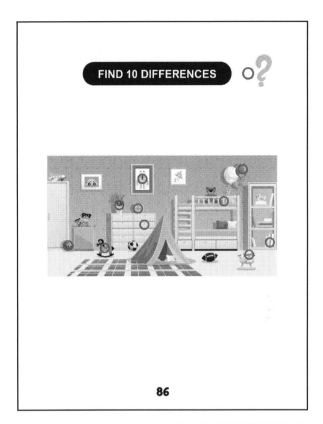

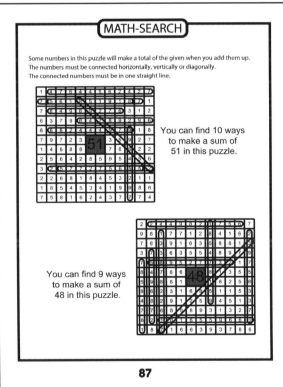

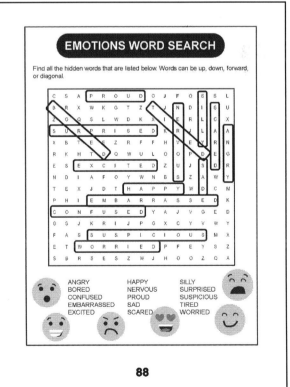

Answer Key

SCRAMBLED WORDS

Unscramble the spelling words that are animals.

TKINET	KITTEN
EOMYNK	MONKEY
USEOM	MOUSE
GREIT	TIGER
EBRA	BEAR
FLOBUAF	BUFFALO
LAFC	CALF
ALMCE	CAMEL
RBEZA	ZEBRA
EERD	DEER

89

FOLLOW THE PATTERNS

Color the donut that comes next.

90

BIRDS CROSSWORD

Complete the crossword puzzle by filling in the appropriate letters with the help of pictures given below.

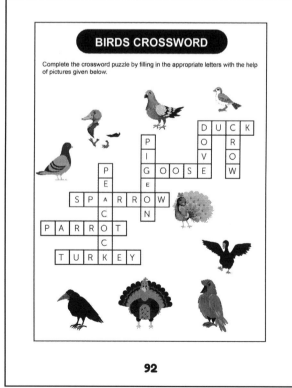

92

112

CONGRATULATIONS!

Excellent work! I am sure that there were some obstacles along the way, but you persisted and finished the activities! Hooray!

I also want to give a HUGE THANKS to our staff at Kids Castle Press for making these books a reality. It wouldn't have been possible without them. Feel free to visit our website below to show them some love!

In addition, if you'd like us to send you more free content to print out, you can do so by visiting our website: www.kidscastlepress.com

To add a cherry on top... You can email us for a chance to win a free physical copy of our next book: info@kidscastlepress.com
Don't miss out as we won't be doing this forever... it's a limited time only!

Lastly, if you like this book, would you be so kind as to drop me a review on Amazon?

Thank you very much!

Jennifer L. Trace

ACTIVITY PRO
CERTIFICATE

_____

Date: _____   **Signed:** _____

Made in the USA
Middletown, DE
23 November 2022